Sam wanted a cake.
Dad said, 'No, Sam.'

1

Sam wanted a video.
Dad said, 'No, Sam.'

Sam wanted to play his drum.
Mum said, 'No, Sam.'

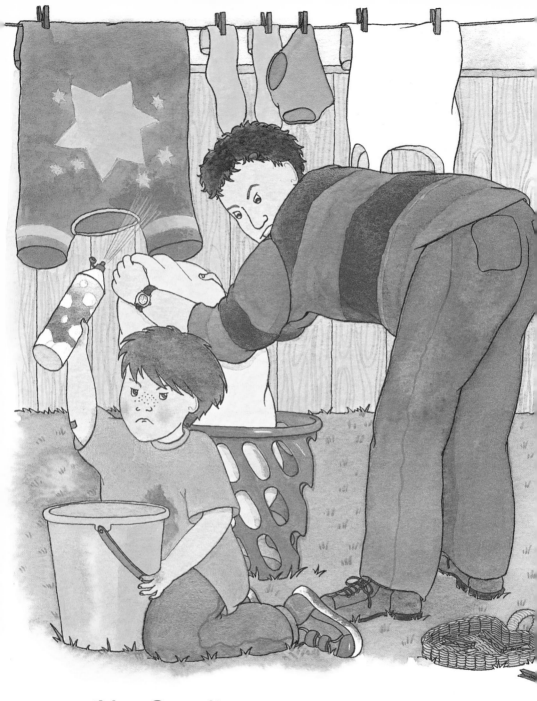

'No, Sam!'

'No, Sam! No, Sam!'

Sam was fed up.

He went to see Rosie.

Sam said, 'Let's play with water.'

Rosie said, 'Yes, Sam!'

Sam said, 'Let's make mud!'
Rosie said, 'Yes, Sam!'

Sam said, 'Let's make a mess.'

Rosie said, 'Yes, Sam!
Yes, Sam! Yes, Sam!'